P[illegible] Pocket Puzzle Book

Written by Alex Frith and Sam Lake

Designed by Zoe Wray

Illustrated by

Peter Allen, Mattia Cerato, Laurent Kling,
Rory Walker, Benedetta Giaufret and Enrica Rusinà

Which ship has the bigger crew?

The pirate crew of the *Ghostly Galleon* are all dressed in blue.

The buccaneer crew of the *Murderous Man o'War* are all dressed in red.

These pirates are all lined up in a special order...

Alberto the Beastly

Bernardo the Cruel

Carlos the Destroyer

Domingo the Evil

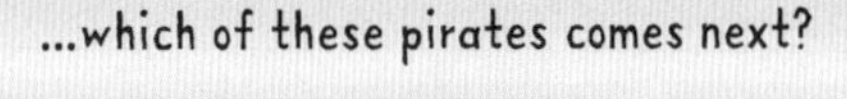

...which of these pirates comes next?

Ernesto the Foul

Django the Savage

Enrico the Fearless

Can you spot the two matching figureheads?

Follow the lines to find out which ship's cannonball struck the *Santa Ana.*
A
Nina
B
Pinta

C
Queen of the East
Santa Ana

Dirk Chivers
Oliver La Buse
Anne Bonny
Calico Jack
Jean Lafitte
Red Legs Greaves
Who stole my ship?
Black Bart
Thomas Tew

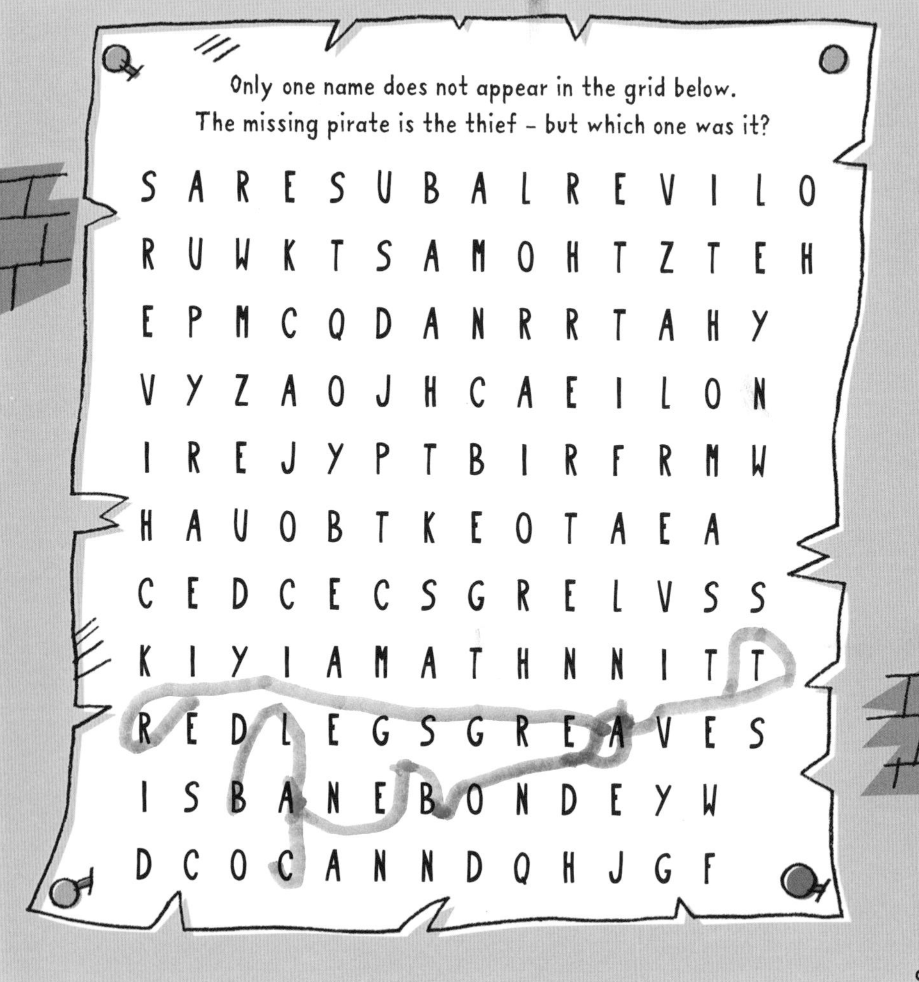
Only one name does not appear in the grid below.
The missing pirate is the thief – but which one was it?
S A R E S U B A L R E V I L O
R U W K T S A M O H T Z T E H
E P M C Q D A N R R T A H Y
V Y Z A O J H C A E I L O N
I R E J Y P T B I R F R M W
H A U O B T K E O T A E A
C E D C E C S G R E L V S S
K I Y I A M A T H N N I T T
R E D L E G S G R E A V E S
I S B A N E B O N D E Y W
D C O C A N N D Q H J G F

Which of these pirates has just buried a treasure chest?

...And which of them is digging it up again?

Can you identify the **pirate** and the **pirate hunter** hiding out in this sailors' tavern?

THE PIRATE

- wears a three-pointed hat
- goes everywhere with his first mate, Bearded Bill
- likes to keep warm
- likes wearing stripes

THE PIRATE HUNTER

- stays away from parrots
- hates beards
- thinks green is lucky
- carries a sword

Captain Pilchard has seen three ships approaching. Which of the four views on the right shows what he can see?

A
B
C
D

Mutinous Micah
12
7
9

Which animal will be first to catch Mutinous Micah after he jumps?
Find the number of the beast...

- The number is even.
- It's divisible by four, but not three.
- It's less than the number of shark fins in the scene.

Are there more cannons... ...or muskets ...on board this ship?

Fill in the grid with these four treasures. Each row, column and 4-square box must contain one of each.

Candlestick

Necklace

You can write the names in, or draw pictures of each treasure.

Goblet

Ring

Yargh!
Yargh! a-yaargh Yeargh argh?
Singood
Sinbad
Yagh!
YAARRRRgh YRgh!
YRRgh YRgh!
yaARGH!

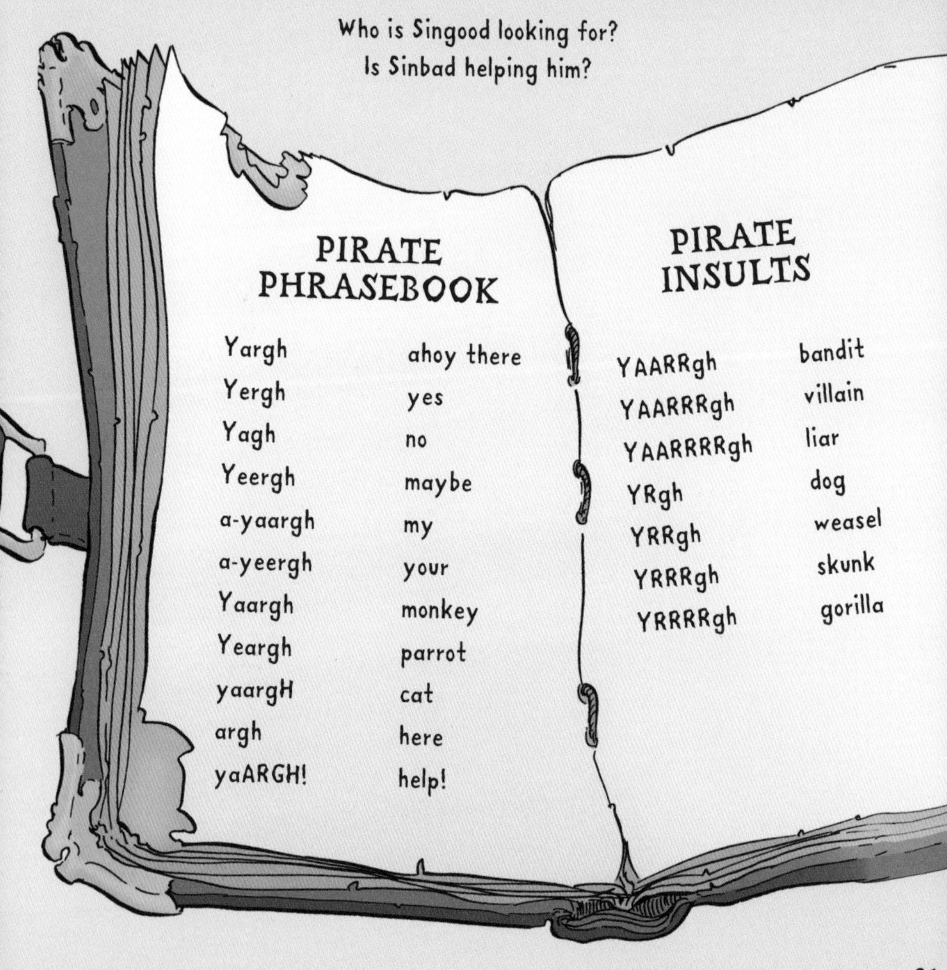
Who is Singood looking for?
Is Sinbad helping him?
PIRATE PHRASEBOOK
Yargh ahoy there
Yergh yes
Yagh no
Yeergh maybe
a-yaargh my
a-yeergh your
Yaargh monkey
Yeargh parrot
yaargH cat
argh here
yaARGH! help!
PIRATE INSULTS
YAARRgh bandit
YAARRRgh villain
YAARRRRgh liar
YRgh dog
YRRgh weasel
YRRRgh skunk
YRRRRgh gorilla

Which is Roger's ship?
Clue: look for the matching flag.

Which treasure chest will please all the pirates?
A
B
C
D
I want red jewels!
I hate silver coins!
I want a crown!
I'm scared of animals!

Can you help Dirty Duncan find the treasure chest?

Line up the sails to spell out a pirate phrase.

Clue: each buccaneer has an eye patch and a cutlass;
each privateer has a scar and a pistol.

How many **buccaneers** and **privateers** can you see at this party?

Helmsman
Herman
Help Helmsman Herman find his
way through the port back to
his ship, *Black Bolt*.

Black Bolt
Avoid smiling sharks, firing cannons, spouting whales and waving mermaids...

This old Spanish gold coin is known as a *peso de ocho* or 'piece of eight'.

Which of these eight pieces does not come from the 'piece of eight' on the left?

Can you find all these pirate ship parts hidden in the sail?

MAP	SAIL
MAST	DECK
WHEEL	CROWS NEST
RIGGING	JOLLY ROGER

Clue: the words can be read left to right, right to left, top to bottom or diagonally.

F W I G U A S
P E T S E N S W O R C D U
A G U R O G M N H K E S M
M E A O N L E C L A H
O D L I A S E H S C E
J I G O N O P E E T B O J
N G P W E P G H A K L M
L I Q G Q O P W C D A
L R S R J O L L Y R O G E R C
S A I N U S R I S G R Y D E D
W P

Jim is trapped in a barrel of apples. Help him eat his way out, starting with the red apple. Watch out! The apples with spots are poisonous.

Fill in the grid with these four jewels. Each row, column, and 4-square box must contain one of each.

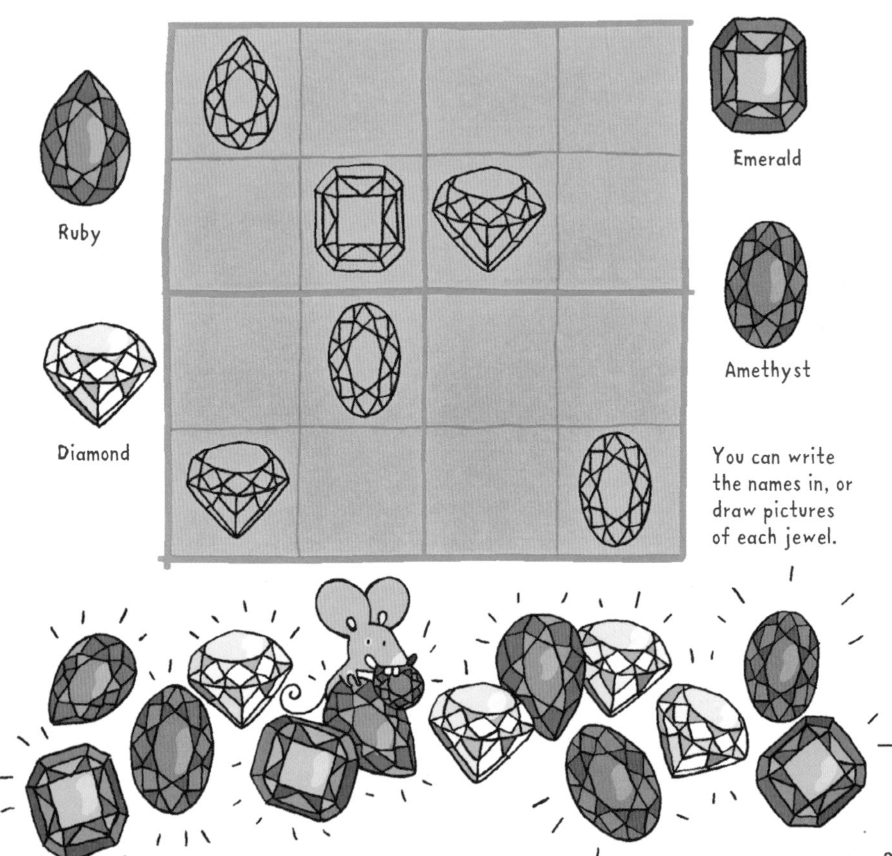

Which missing object has fallen overboard?
Clue: all the other objects are visible in this picture.
I've lost my hook, my pocket watch and my map.
Where's my cutlass, my telescope and my cheese?
I've lost my pistol, my goblet, my cat and my hat!

Jonah
Pierre
Jake
Ahab
Horatio
Erik

Can you guess which instrument each pirate is playing?

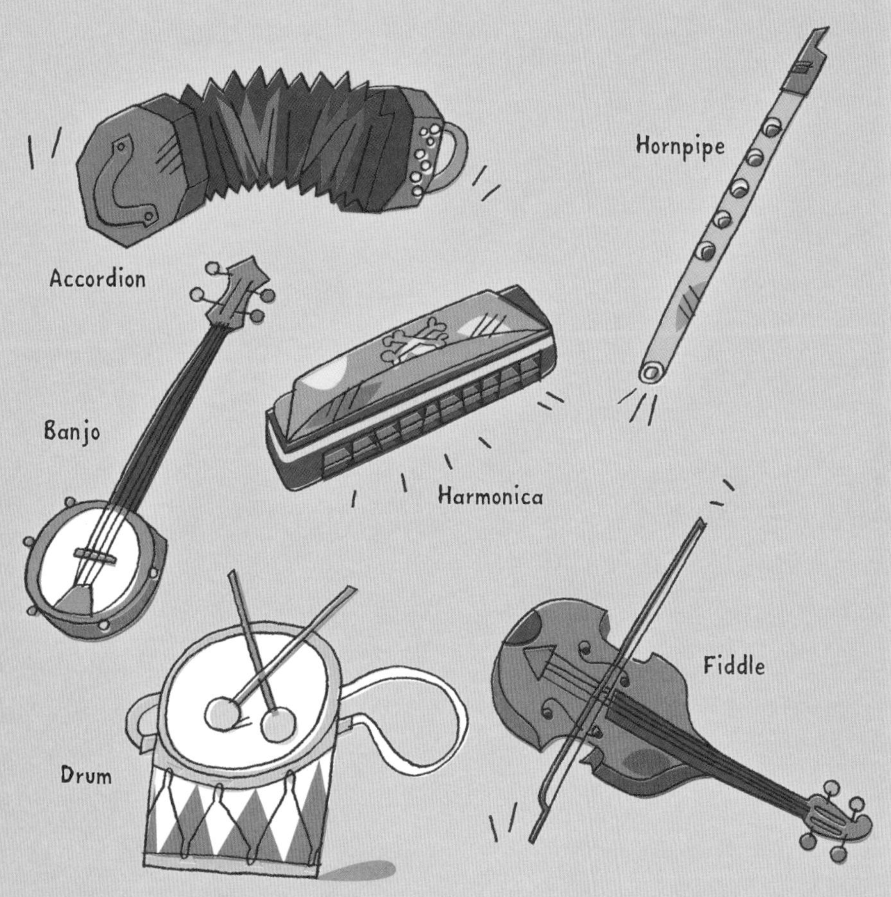

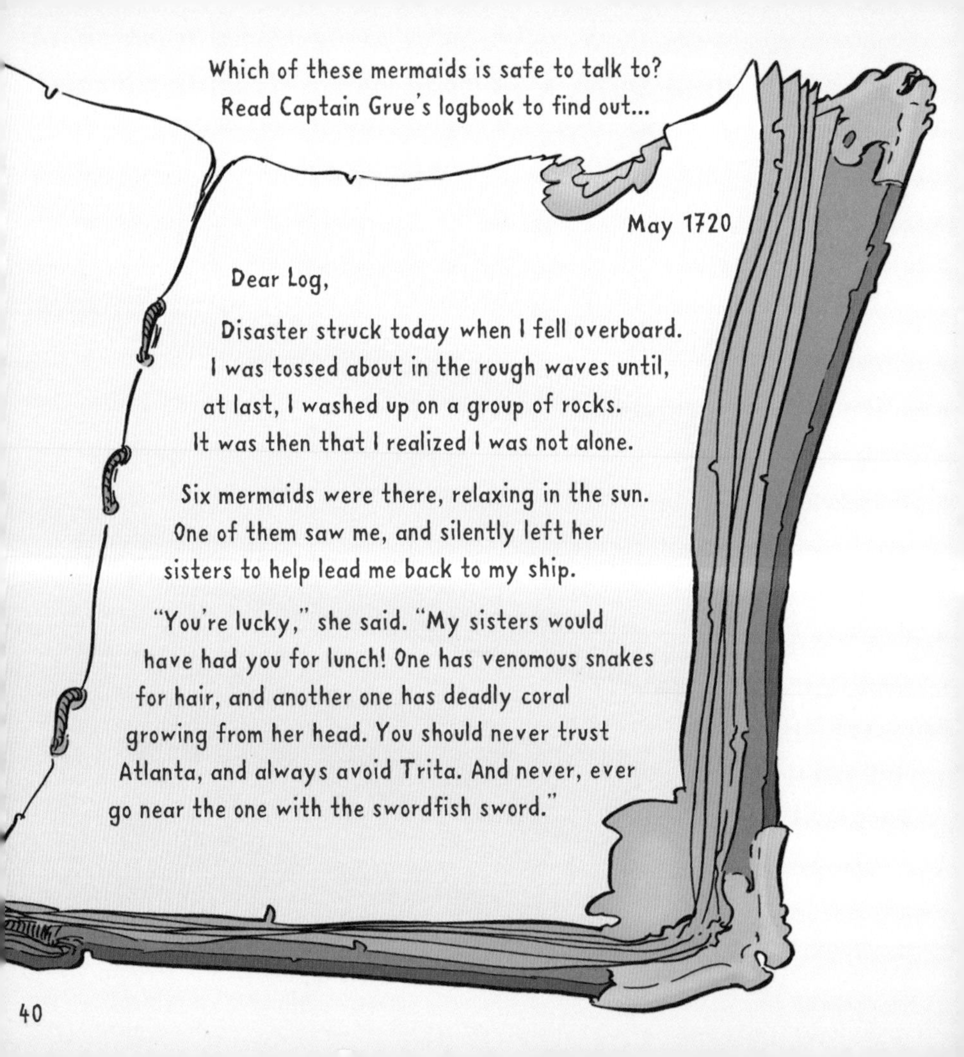

Which of these mermaids is safe to talk to?
Read Captain Grue's logbook to find out...

May 1720

Dear Log,

Disaster struck today when I fell overboard. I was tossed about in the rough waves until, at last, I washed up on a group of rocks. It was then that I realized I was not alone.

Six mermaids were there, relaxing in the sun. One of them saw me, and silently left her sisters to help lead me back to my ship.

"You're lucky," she said. "My sisters would have had you for lunch! One has venomous snakes for hair, and another one has deadly coral growing from her head. You should never trust Atlanta, and always avoid Trita. And never, ever go near the one with the swordfish sword."

Scylla
Ceta
Trita
Galena
Nema
Atlanta

Can you unscramble the words to reveal today's rations?

Which parrot is different from all the others?

Which ship can move fastest in this pirate boat race?
Speed is measured in sail power:
1 sail = 1 sail power
2 pairs of oars = 1 sail power
1 motor = 4 sail power
A
B
C

D
E
FINISH
LINE
F
G

Pirates attack the Royal Navy by moonlight.

Can you find eight differences between these two scenes?

The letters on these gold coins spell out six treasures, including 'gold'. Continue the line through the coins to identify all the treasures and reach the end.

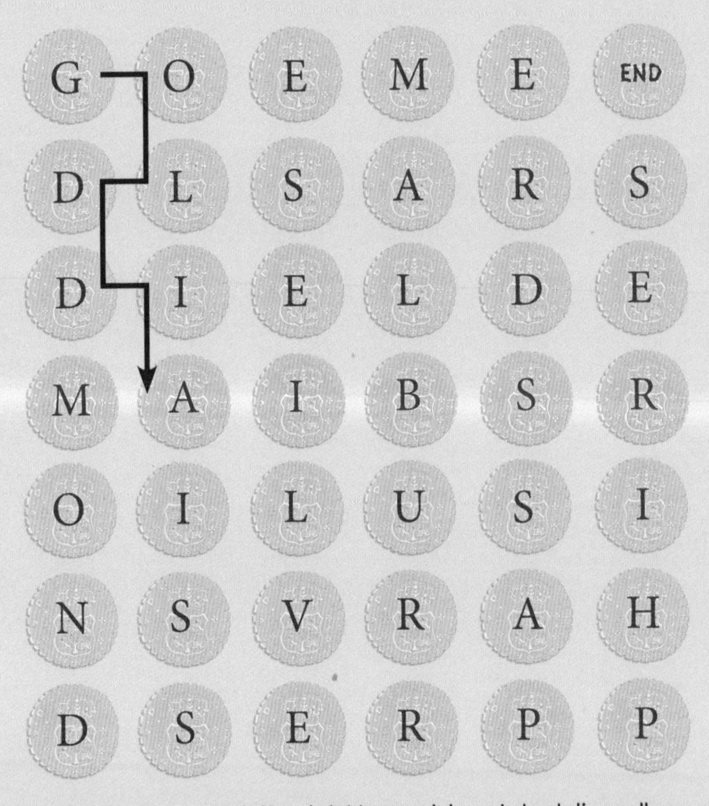

Clue: the line can go left and right, up and down, but not diagonally.

Which are there more of – goblets or necklaces?

Long John Gold has found a key, but which treasure chest will it unlock? Follow the instructions below to guide him around the island.

Clue: after each encounter, keep going in the same direction until you reach the next instruction.

C

A

B

Start here.

Fill in the missing letters to reveal the items in this pirate market.

C_N_ON__LLS	H__KS
E__P__CH_S	P_G L_GS
_U_LA__ES	_IST__S

This spark is lighting its way along a trail of gunpowder, but which barrel will explode?

Which two pirates are wearing identical outfits?

Fill in the grid with these four animals. Each row, column, and 4-square box must contain one of each.

Can you guess the correct historical sequence for these four pirate ships?

How many of these things will help the floundering pirates stay afloat?

There are seven invisible pirates on this island. Can you guess where they are?

Sixteen men on a dead man's chest...

...can you find eight differences between these two scenes?

How many members of Captain Mutt's crew can you spot in this busy port town?

Members of Captain Mutt's crew wear vertical striped shirts, carry swords, and never wear eye patches.

Find and cross off all the words from the message above in the shipwreck on the right. The remaining letters will reveal the location of the missing map.

B N

D C A

A N J U D O O M

S I O E T R O P

R H F N R W L E I M

L D A V E Y O E A H I

P E F R T S E H C L S L

R A U M K R E K C O L D S X X

D M T R E A S U R E X I

B U R I E D E L O T S M

Clue: the words can be read left to right, right to left, top to bottom, or diagonally.

Which boat has Sailor Steve untied from its mooring?

C
D
E
F

What's inside these barrels
in the hold?
Unscramble the letters
on the labels.
KUTMESS
NANCONSLLAB
TALS
BITICUSS
RANGOES
WUNPODGER

Find the secret pirate lair. The island is south of all the whirlpools. It has two trees and no buildings.

One-eyed McMullan
Lips Lehane
Crossbones McGroo
Cutlass o'Donoghue
Whitey Logan
Grrr! Those pesky monkeys have done it again!

Can you match each thieving monkey with the pirate it has stolen from?

Captain Wartnose loved his gold.
You can read all about him below.

all day and all night, and chased
away any who came too close with
a wave of his knife and a chilling
stare from his one beady eye.
But Wartnose was an unlucky pirate. In a
battle with his rival, Captain Shin, a stray
cannonball hit *Trident's* hull. The boat shook, the
hold burst open, and Wartnose's gold poured out
into the sea, never to be seen again. Or did it?
What really happened
to Wartnose's lost gold?
Can you find the truth
hidden in the text?

Fill in the grid with these four coins. Each row, column and 4-square box must contain one of each.

You can write in the names, or draw pictures of each coin.

Which boat will win the race?

Here's a clue:

A corsair and a privateer are as fast as one buccaneer in a boat.
Two corsairs are equal to one privateer.

An old castaway is watching a pirate crew relax.

Can you find eight differences between these two scenes?

Oh no! There are only two hammocks. Which pirate will be left out when all his chores are done?
Follow the routes shown, and add on time for each chore to find out.
One-armed Robert
Redbeard
Harry Brow

It takes:

1 minute to turn the capstan and raise the anchor

2 minutes to feed the cat

2 minutes to scrub the deck

3 minutes to climb the rigging

Find the captain
of the *Golden Narwhal.*
He has a beard, is holding a scroll
and hates parrots.

Golden Narwhal

Match these sea creatures to the objects they are named after.

Which of the ships from A to F comes next in this sequence?

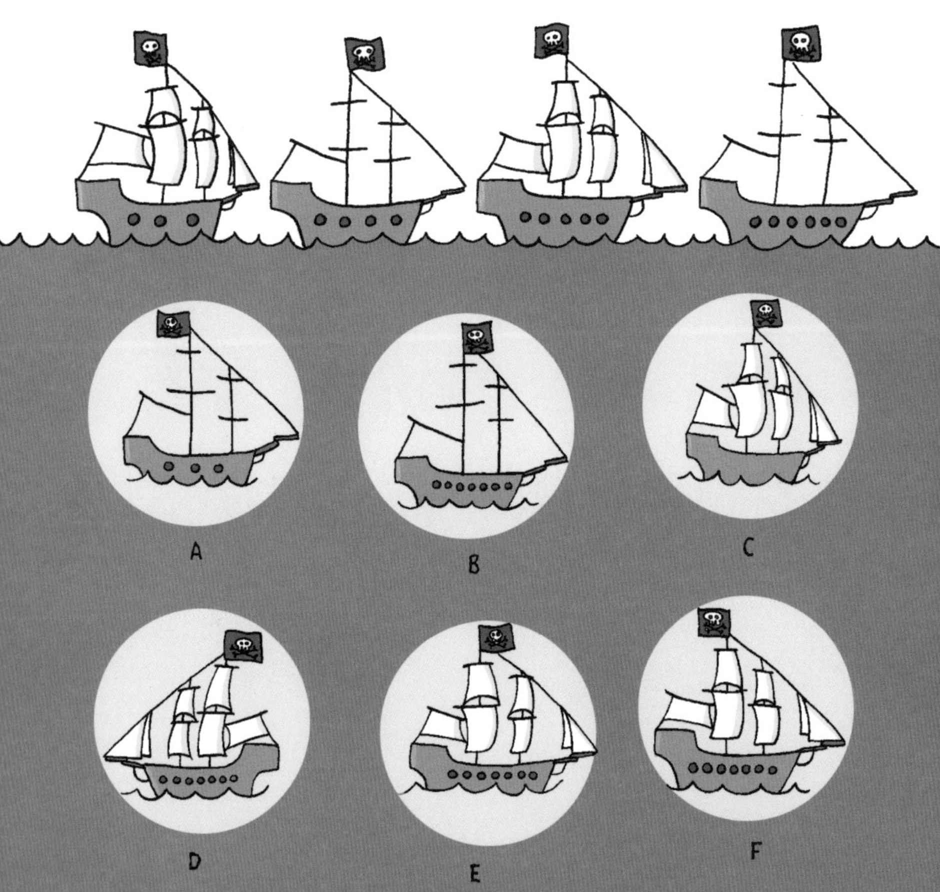

These pirates are singing a sea shanty. All the words are the same – only the alphabets used to write them are different. Can you work out how the song ends?

νοτ μντιλ ωε'χε ρομνκ ομφσελχεσ υ τφευσμφε эπεστ!
≈¤π V≈πł× Łþ'¦þ ž¤V≈≠ ¤VʃšþX¦þš ∞ πʃþ∞šVʃþ Ýðþšπ!
___ U____ WE'VE F_U_D _U____V__ _ _____U__ C____!

There are six invisible
pirates in this tavern.
Can you guess where
they all are?

Find eight rats and one stowaway in this ship's hold.

Cap'n Aaargh is the most popular doll on the high seas. How many complete Cap'n Aaargh dolls can you make from these parts?

It's so murky, I can't see! Guide me safely to the treasure chest, avoiding dangerous creatures blocking my path.

Look out for seagulls and snakes.
START
Scamper up the rope
Help! I need to find a safe way around the ship's wheel to reach my crackers.

I'm not the spy!
The real spy has a red bandana, no tattoos and a scar on his face.
Square-jawed Sven
Grumpy Gutteridge
Yellow Yorick
Wide-eyed Wilson
Breeches Brewster
Help Captain Cut-throat identify the real spy.

The names on the pirates are all mixed up. Use the clues at the bottom to decide which name belongs to which pirate.

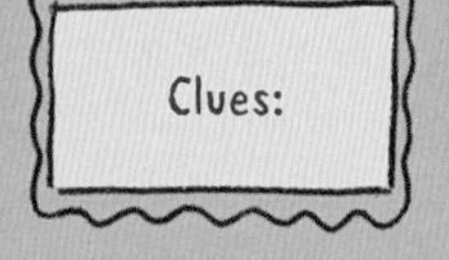

Grace O'Malley carries a pair of pistols.

Ching Shi wields a curved sword.

Henry Morgan was a wealthy man with a feathered hat.

Sayyida al Hurra
scared off her enemies with a long-barrelled musket.

Captain Kidd
wore the white wig of a British Navy officer.

'Black' Sam Bellamy
had long black hair tied in a pony tail.

Arrange the letters on the barrels to find a message for the stranded pirate.

Yaargh! I'm rich!
Help me find: 6 red rubies, 5 blue sapphires, 3 green emeralds, and 4 white pearl necklaces.

Follow the instructions below to lead the merchant ship to the only safe island in the sea.

Steer east to evade sea serpents.

Steer north to escape from whirlpools.

Steer south to flee from volcanoes.

Steer west to outsail pirates.

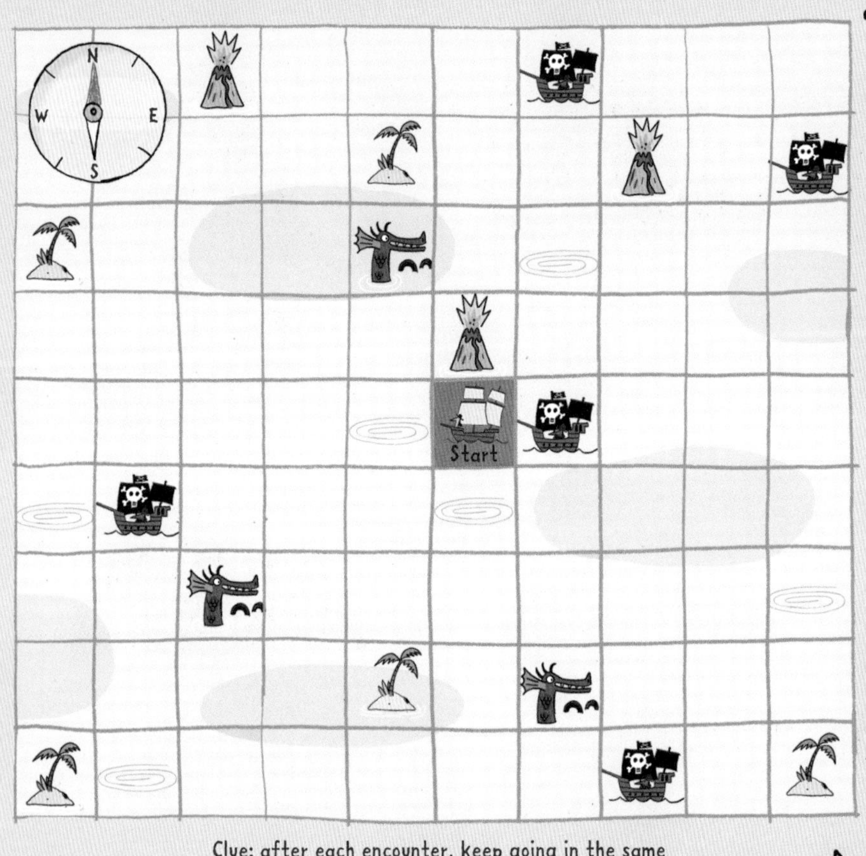

Clue: after each encounter, keep going in the same direction until you reach the next instruction.

Who is the real Blackbeard? He wore a three-cornered hat; he didn't have an eyepatch; he hid lit fuses inside his bushy, black beard.

Put these pictures in the correct order to tell a story.

Can you find:

A sleeping cat

15 sausages

A mouse with grog

5 cutlasses

1 cockerel

13 worms

This is the flag of the fearsome pirate Captain Blackgizzard.

Which part below does not belong to the flag?

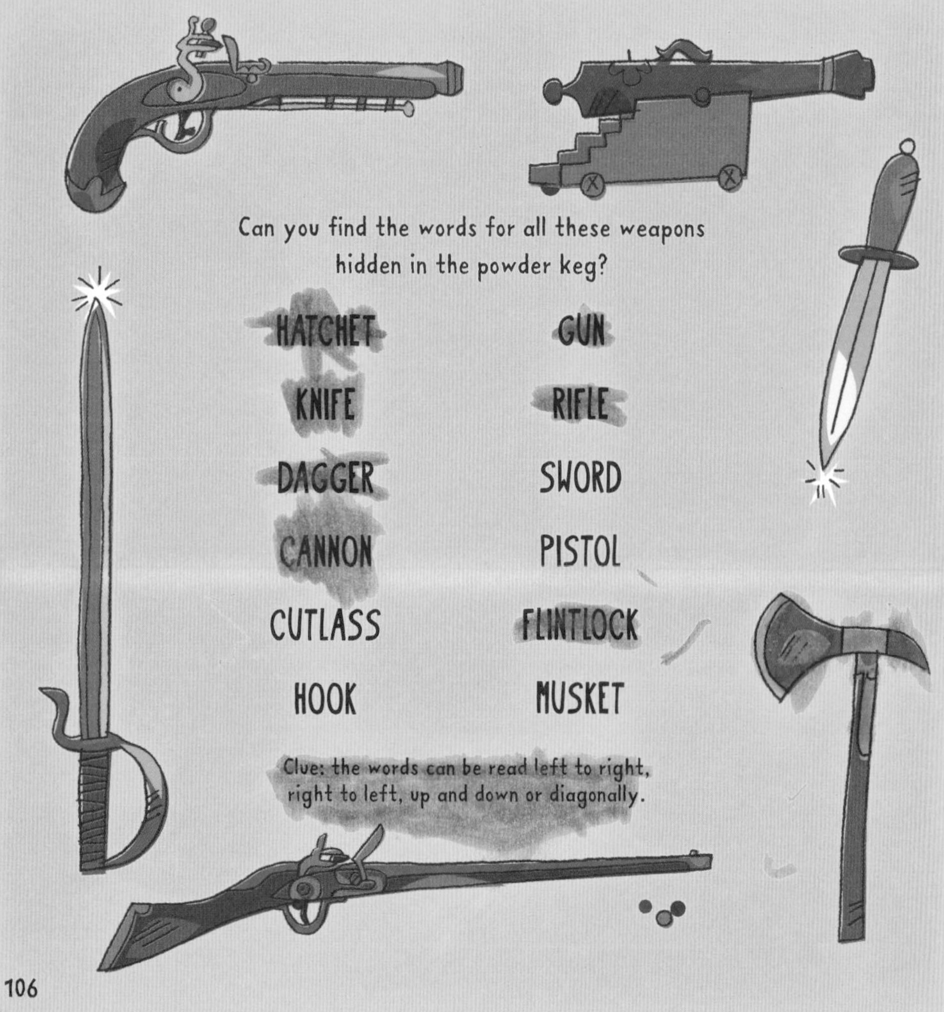

Can you find the words for all these weapons hidden in the powder keg?

HATCHET	GUN
KNIFE	RIFLE
DAGGER	SWORD
CANNON	PISTOL
CUTLASS	FLINTLOCK
HOOK	MUSKET

Clue: the words can be read left to right, right to left, up and down or diagonally.

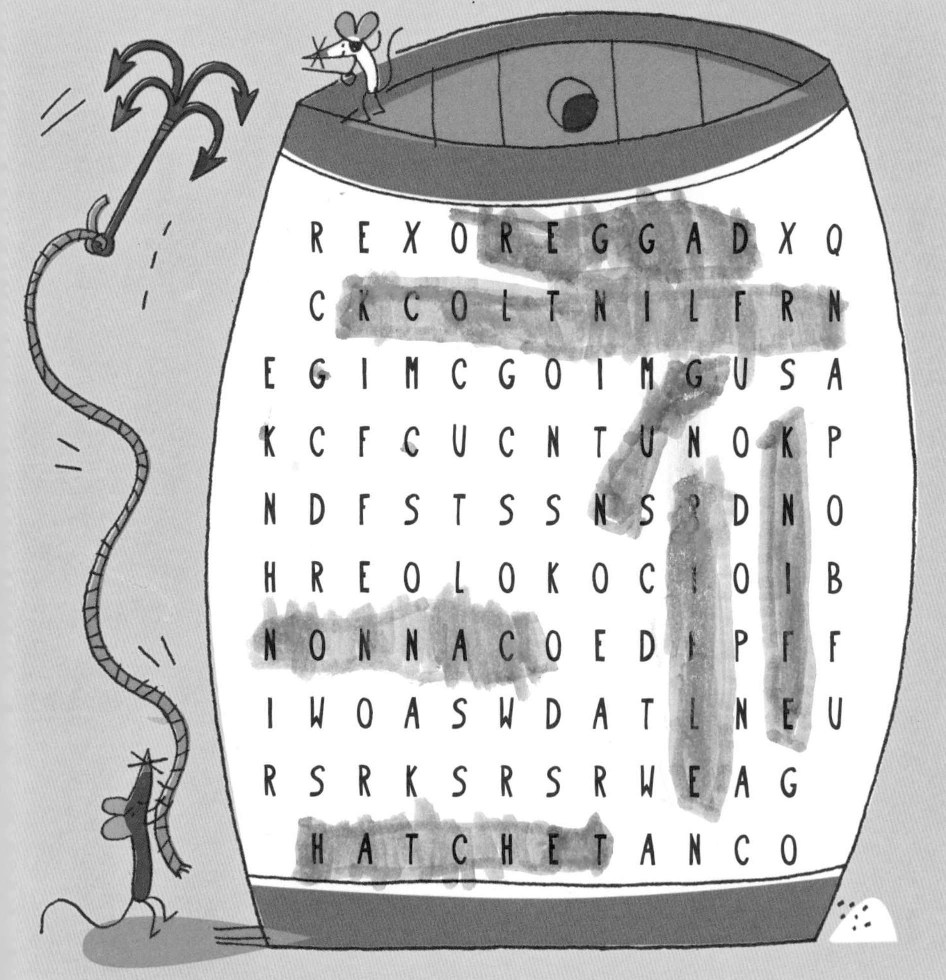
R E X O R E G G A D X Q
C K C O L T N I L F R N
E G I M C G O I M G U S A
K C F C U C N T U N O K P
N D F S T S S N S R D N O
H R E O L O K O C I O I B
N O N N A C O E D F P F F
I W O A S W D A T L N E U
R S R K S R S R W E A G
H A T C H E T A N C O

Captain Barbauld has spent exactly 13 gold coins to buy two of these objects. Which items did he buy?

These sea serpents have the names of six sea creatures written along their bodies. Can you find them all?
D O L P
I N S H A
K W H A L
P I R A N H
T A R F I S
E A H O R E
Clue: some of the letters are hidden underwater.

Time tourists have arrived in the great golden age of pirates. How many modern day people and objects can you find on this ship?

Answers

Pages 2-3

There are 11 blue pirates but only 9 red buccaneers. So the *Ghostly Galleon* has the bigger crew.

Page 4

The next pirate in order should be Enrico the Fearless.

Page 5

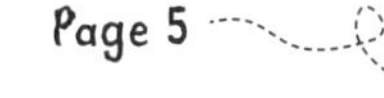

Pages 6-7

Ship C, *Queen of the East*

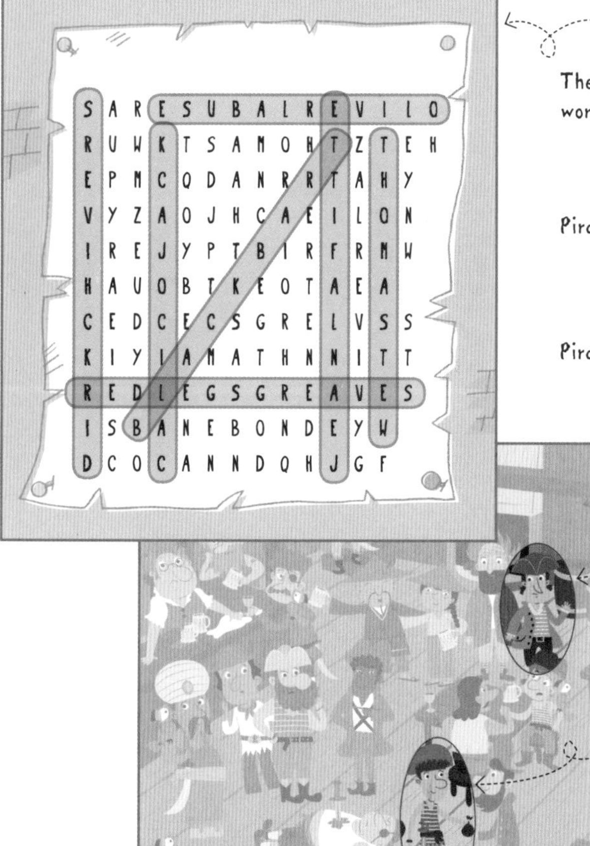

Pages 8-9

The pirate missing from the wordsearch is Anne Bonny.

Page 10

Pirate C buried the treasure.

Page 11

Pirate B found the treasure.

Pages 12-13

Pirate

Pirate hunter

Pages 14-15

D is the correct view through the telescope.

Pages 16-17

Shark number 4 will catch Mutinous Micah.

Page 18

There are 11 muskets but 14 cannons.

Page 19

Page 22

This is Roger's ship

Pages 20-21

Singood is looking for his parrot. Sinbad has hidden the parrot in a box on his ship.

Page 23

Only chest B will please all four pirates.

Page 24

Page 25

The sails spell out 'pieces of eight'.

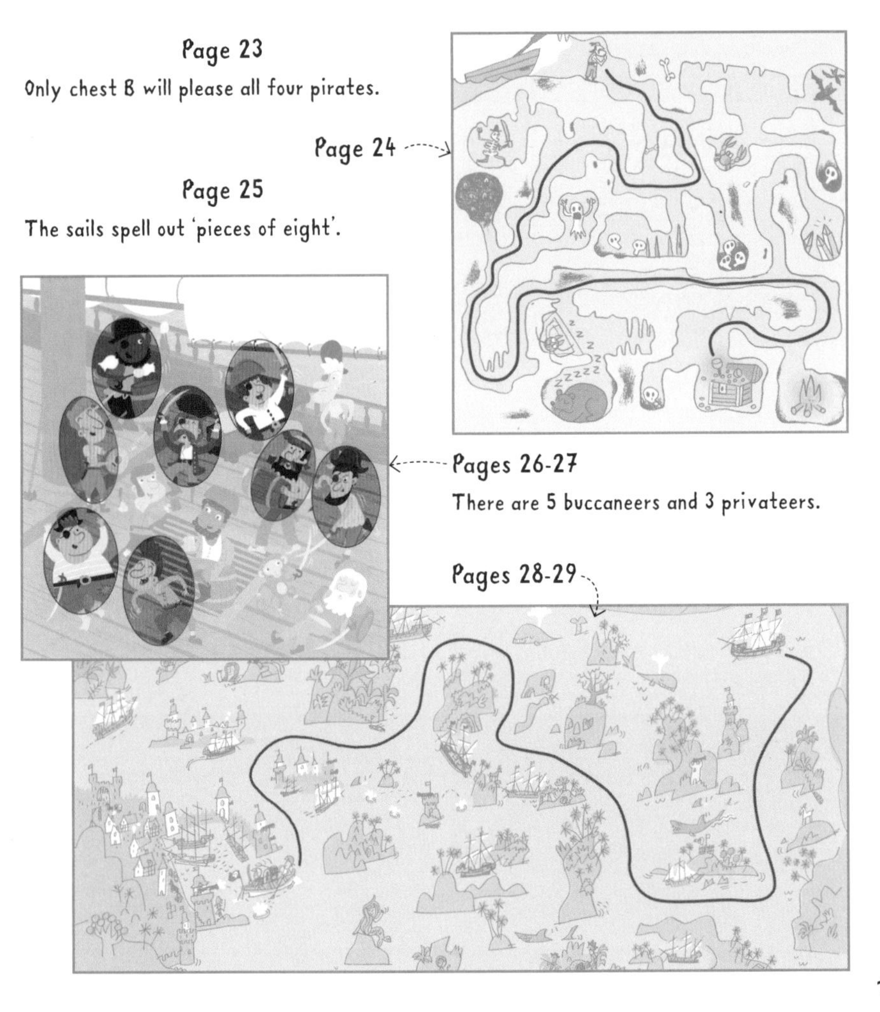

Pages 26-27

There are 5 buccaneers and 3 privateers.

Pages 28-29

Pages 30-31

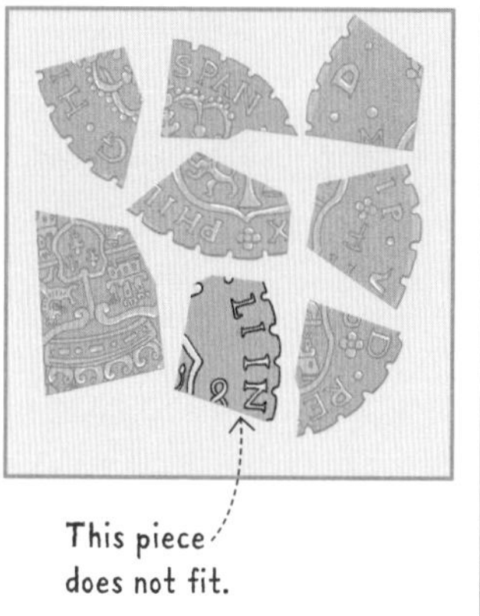

Pages 32-33

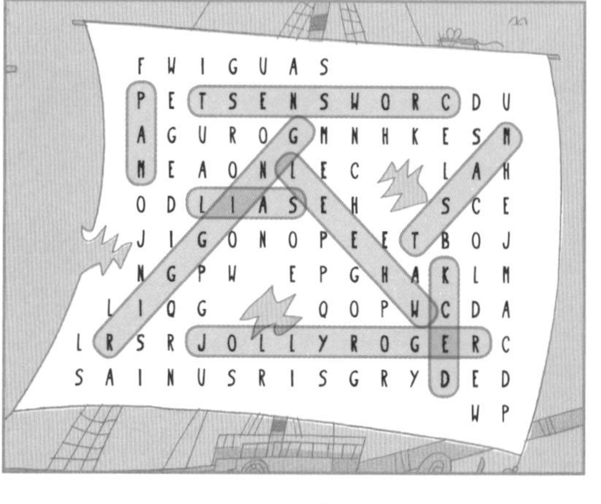

Page 34

Page 35

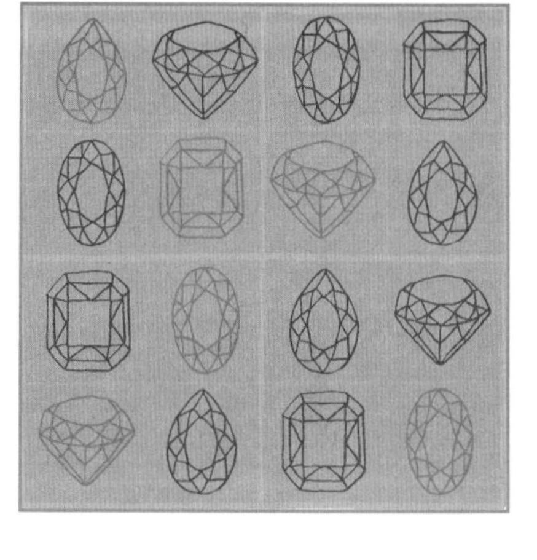

Pages 36-37

The hat has fallen overboard.

Pages 38-39

Jonah is playing the fiddle.
Pierre is playing the banjo.
Jake is playing the drum.
Ahab is playing the harmonica.
Horatio is playing the hornpipe.
Erik is playing the accordion.

Pages 40-41

Only Galena is safe to talk to.

Page 42

The unscrambled menu reads:
stale bread
rotten cabbage
roast rats
warm beer

Page 43

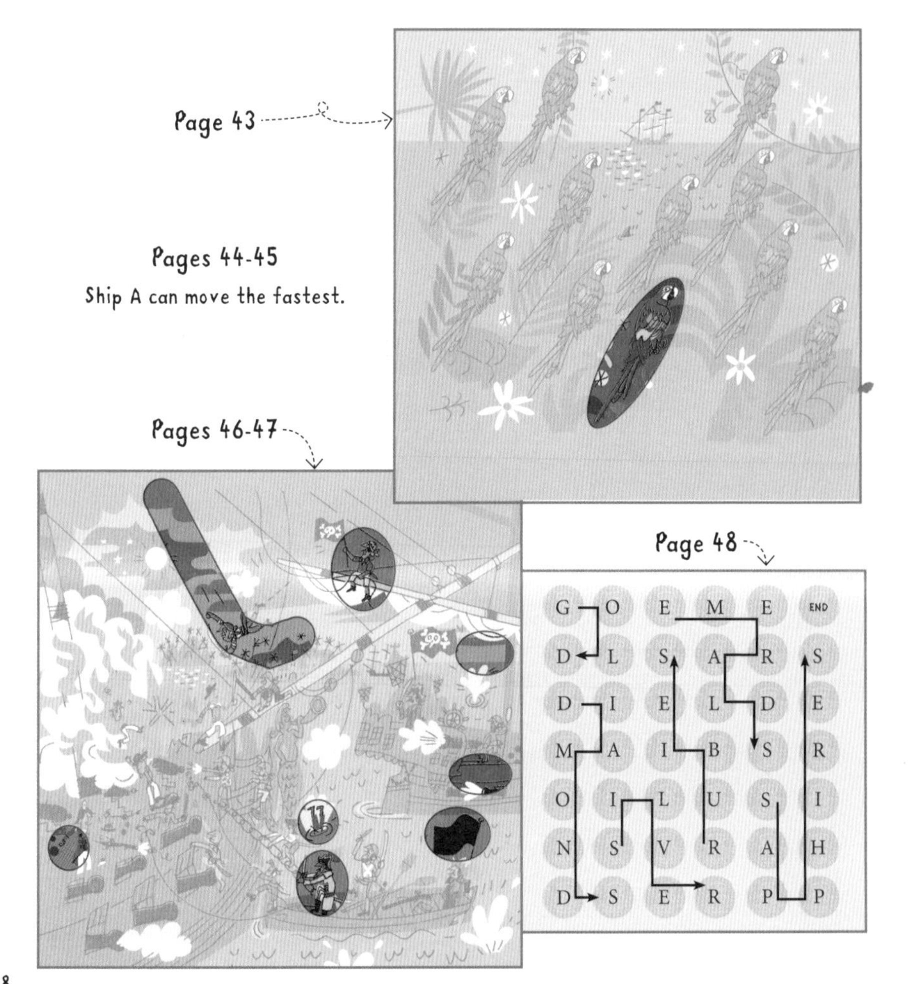

Pages 44-45

Ship A can move the fastest.

Pages 46-47

Page 48

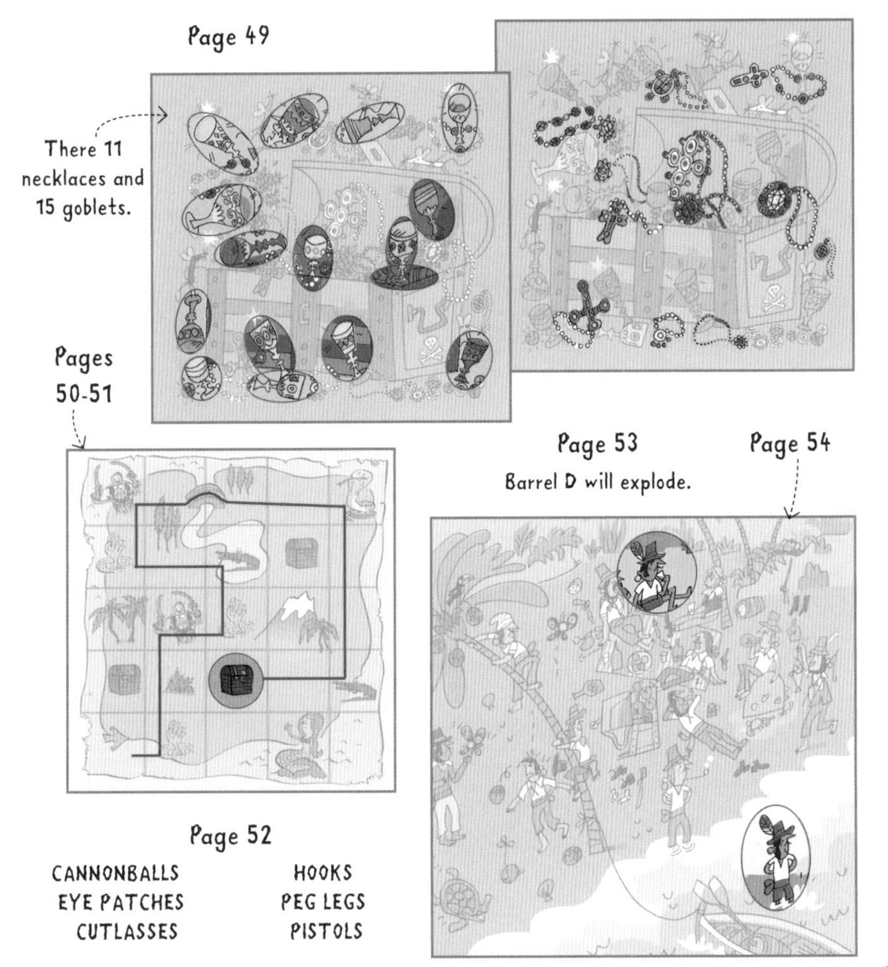
Page 49
There 11
necklaces and
15 goblets.
Pages
50-51
Page 52
CANNONBALLS
EYE PATCHES
CUTLASSES
HOOKS
PEG LEGS
PISTOLS
Page 53
Barrel D will explode.
Page 54

Page 55

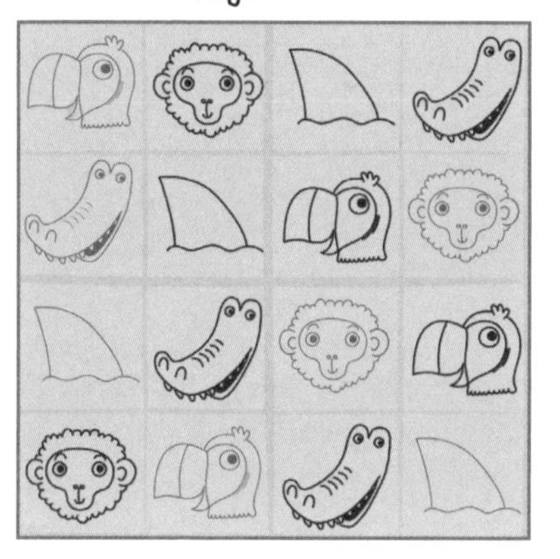

Page 56

The correct sequence is: B (Roman trireme); A (Viking longship); D (17th century galleon); C (modern motor boat).

Page 57

These 5 objects will keep the pirates afloat:

Pages 58-59

Pages 60-61

Pages 62-63

There are six pirates in the port.

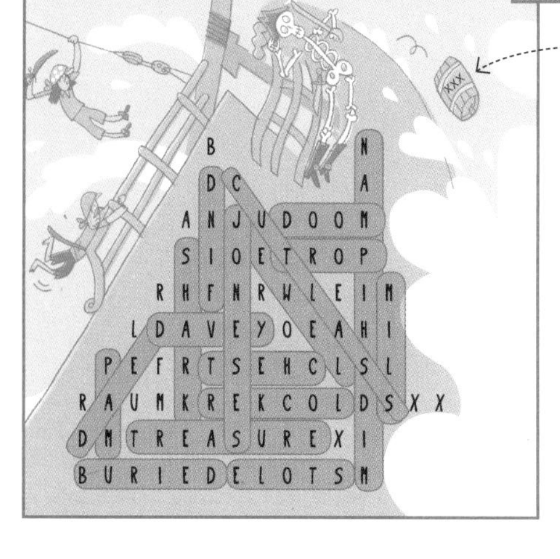

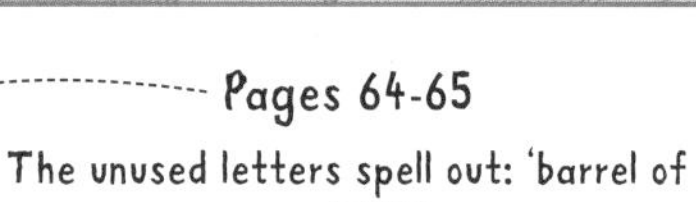

Pages 64-65

The unused letters spell out: 'barrel of rum XXX'.

Pages 66-67

Sailor Steve has untied Boat F.

Page 68

The barrels contain:
muskets, cannonballs, salt, biscuits, oranges, gunpowder.

Page 69

Pages 70-71

Micro has One-eyed McMullan's eye patch.

Pico has Lips Lehane's boot.

Femto has Crossbones McGroo's hat.

Atto has Cutlass O'Donoghue's cutlass.

Nano has Whitey Logan's hook.

Pages 72-73

The smudged letters spell out the sentence: Shin stole Wartnose's gold and retired.

Page 74

Page 75

Boat B will win the race.

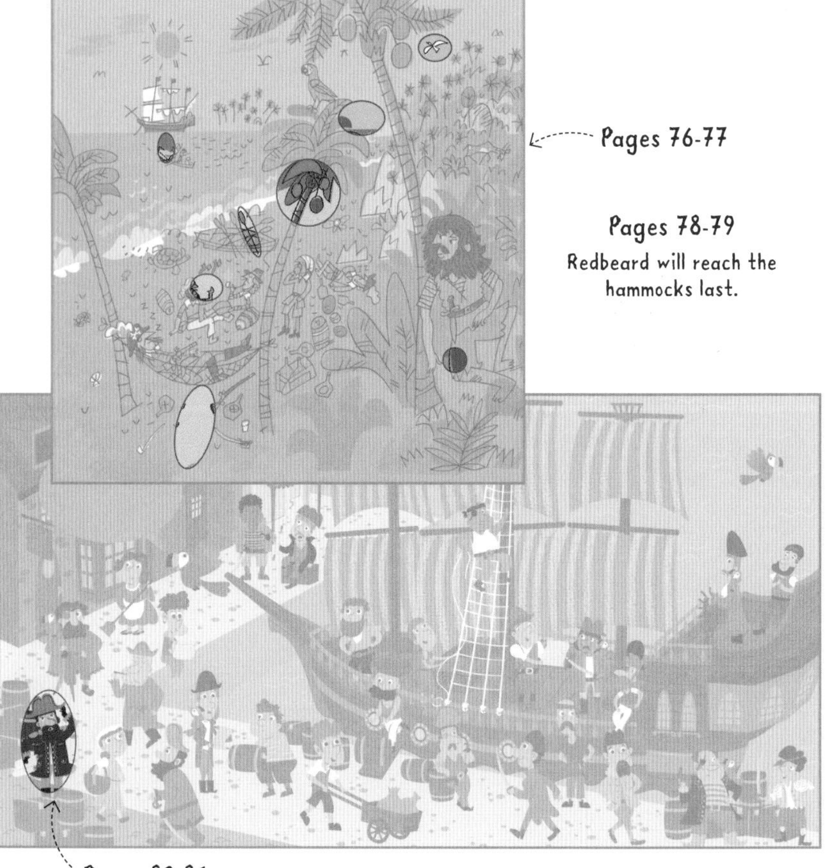

Pages 76-77

Pages 78-79

Redbeard will reach the hammocks last.

Pages 80-81

The captain is here.

Page 82

A5 (starfish), B1 (sawfish), C2 (jellyfish), D4 (swordfish), E3 (hammerhead shark).

Page 83

The next ship in the sequence is F.

Pages 84-85

The next verse of the sea shanty is:

'NOT UNTIL WE'VE FOUND OURSELVES A TREASURE CHEST'.

Pages 86-87

Page 88

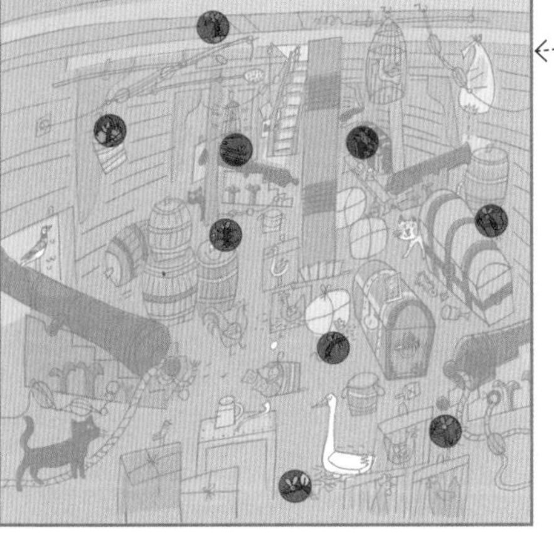

Page 89

You can make 3 complete Cap'n Aaargh dolls.

Page 92

Pages 90-91

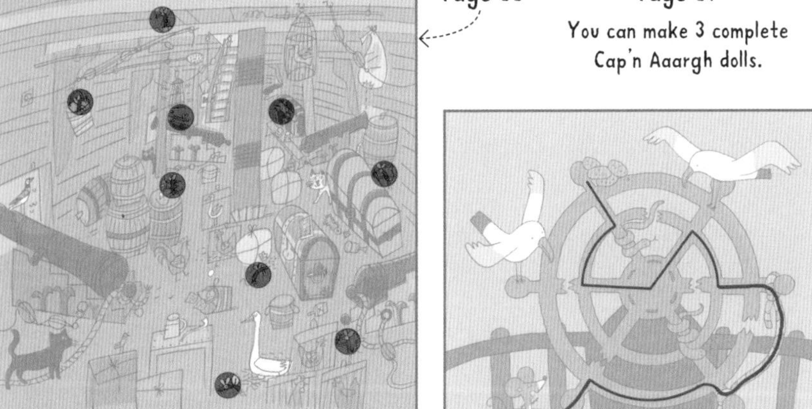

Page 93

The real spy is Yellow Yorick.

Pages 94-95

The pirates are:
A Sayyida al Hurra
B 'Black' Sam Bellamy
C Grace O'Malley
D Henry Morgan
E Ching Shi
F Captain Kidd

Page 96

The barrels spell: 'Do you like rum?'

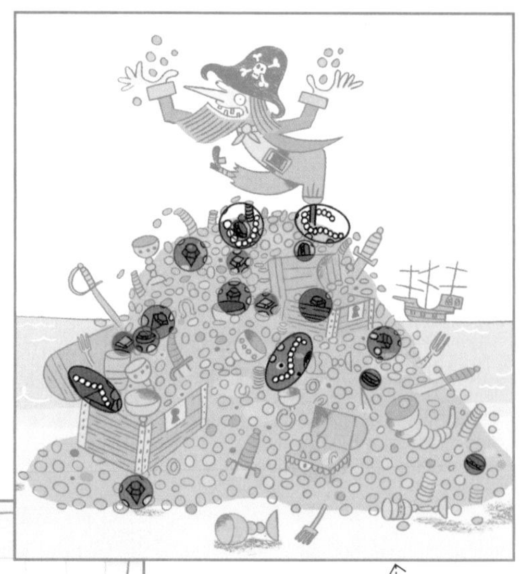

Page 97

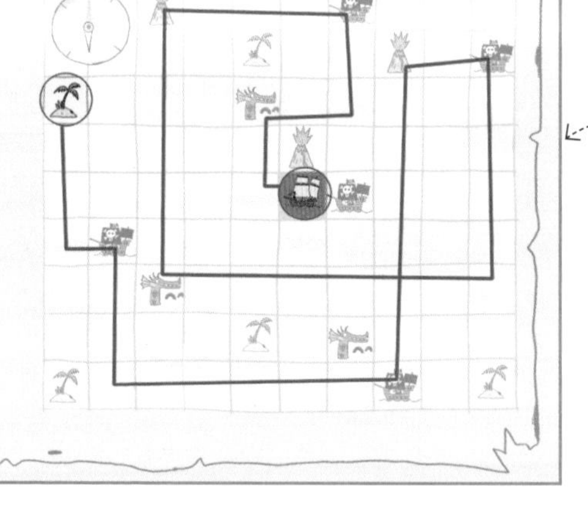

Pages 98-99

Page 100

The real Blackbeard is pirate C.

Page 101

The correct order is DACB.

Pages 102-103

Pages 104-105

This part does not belong:

Pages 106-107

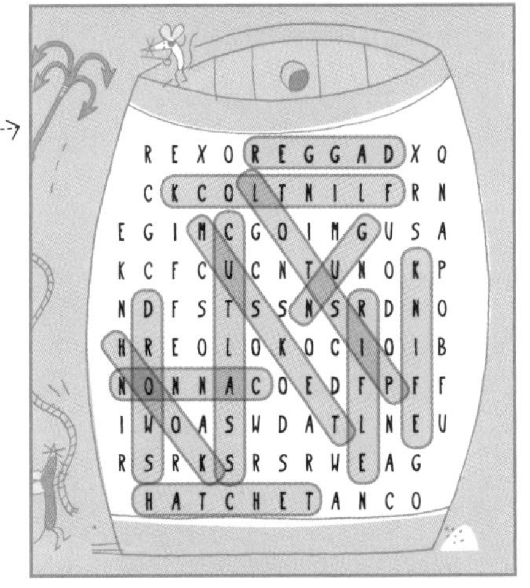

Page 108

Captain Barbauld bought the jewels and the parrot.

Page 109

The sea creatures named are: dolphin; shark; whale; piranha; starfish; seahorse.

Pages 110-111

There are 11 time-lost people or objects on the ship.

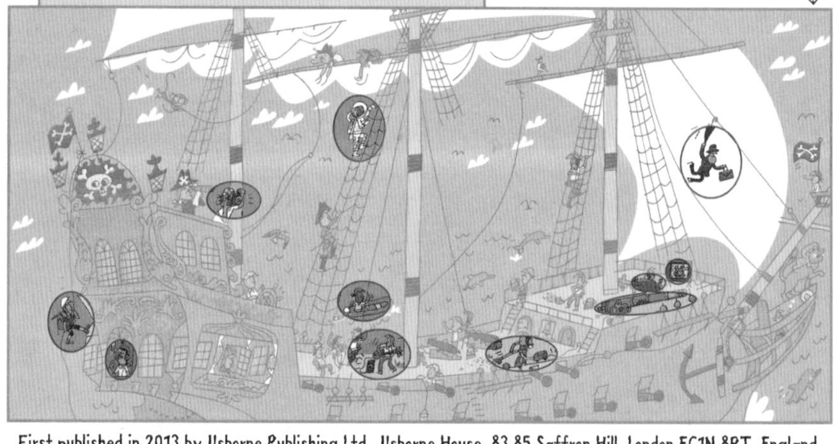

First published in 2013 by Usborne Publishing Ltd., Usborne House, 83-85 Saffron Hill, London EC1N 8RT, England. www.usborne.com